For Emmie, Florrie & Rory...
& Alice, Otty, Donna, Julian,
Laura, Annie, Harry, Beth, Sam,
Hannah, Georgina, Lochie, India,
Georgia, Eddie, Tom, Harriette, Zoe,
Juliette, Louise, Rosie, Tom, Ilaria
& Edward the Bear.

Copyright © 1991 Paula Cloonan
First published 1991 by Blackie and Son Ltd

A CIP Catalogue record for this book is available
from the British Library

ISBN 0-216-93028-6

Blackie & Son Ltd
7 Leicester Place
London WC2H 7BP

First American edition published in 1991 by
Peter Bedrick Books
2112 Broadway
New York, NY 10023

Library of Congress Cataloging-in-Publication Data

Cloonan, Paula
The twelve days of Christmas/Paula Cloonan. - 1st American ed.
Summary: An illustrated version of the Christmas song.
ISBN 0-87226-438-6
1. Folk-songs, English—Texts. 2. Christmas music.
[1. Folk songs - England. 2. Christmas music.] I. Title.

PZ8.3.C585Tw 1991
782.42'1723'0268—dc20   90-26857
                              CIP
                              AC

Printed in Hong Kong by Wing King Tong Co. Ltd.

The TWELVE DAYS of CHRISTMAS

Paula Cloonan

Blackie
London

Bedrick/Blackie
New York

On the first day of Christmas
My true love sent to me
A partridge in a pear tree.

On the second day of Christmas
My true love sent to me
Two turtle doves.

On the third day of Christmas
My true love sent to me
Three french hens.

On the fourth day of Christmas
My true love sent to me
Four calling birds.

On the fifth day of Christmas
My true love sent to me
Five gold rings.

On the sixth day of Christmas
My true love sent to me
Six geese a-laying.

On the seventh day of Christmas
My true love sent to me
Seven swans a-swimming.

On the eighth day of Christmas
My true love sent to me
Eight maids a-milking.

On the ninth day of Christmas
My true love sent to me
Nine drummers drumming.

On the tenth day of Christmas
My true love sent to me
Ten pipers piping.

On the eleventh day of Christmas
My true love sent to me
Eleven ladies dancing.

On the twelfth day of Christmas
My true love sent to me
Twelve lords a-leaping . . .

Eleven ladies dancing,
Ten pipers piping,
Nine drummers drumming,
Eight maids a-milking,
Seven swans a-swimming,
Six geese a-laying,
Five gold rings,
Four calling birds,
Three french hens,
Two turtle doves
And a partridge in a pear tree.